WHAT is ARTEMIS AFRAID of?

Geanne Meta

Illustrated by: Helen Ayle

For my grand dog, Aurora, who is small and unsure of herself
– and my granddaughter, Everly, who is wise beyond her years

This book belongs to

_____

Artemis is a happy little dog with big, brave dreams.

Sometimes she can be afraid
of everything, it seems.

Most days, playing with Glory
Be, Artemis' playful bark is
strong and hearty.

But today she's hiding because her family
is throwing a humungous party!

Artemis is frightened by decorations, loud music, and people who visit.

Glory Be notices her trembling,
"You seem worried. What is it?"

Artemis explains, "Sometimes I have a tummy feeling that warns me of dangers!"

"I understand!" Glory Be replies, "I'll *introduce* you to my friends, so they'll no longer be strangers!"

Artemis ponders,
"Okay, I'll try to be bold.
But what if everyone tries to pet me
and their hands are cold?"

Glory Be reassures her, "You'll sit in my lap when company's here.

If you don't want them to pet you, I'll say 'Not right now.' Do not fear!"

Throughout the whole party,
Glory Be was true to her word.

She held onto Artemis, making
sure her feelings were heard.

Everyone was nice, and once the party was past,
Artemis felt relieved that she wasn't so nervous, at last.

But then Artemis is startled by all the ringy, dingy sounds in the house.

She looks to Glory Be, "I want to be fearless, but I feel helpless as a mouse."

Mom says, "Don't be silly, you scaredy-dog! It's just the dryer!"

But the buzzer startles Artemis and makes her heartbeat go higher!

Glory Be sees the fear that makes Artemis melt.

"It's OK to feel scared." she exclaims,

"Feelings are meant to be FELT!"

"When I feel overwhelmed, I try to clear my mind.

I slow down my breathing to help me unwind.

Practice with me. Breathe
and count – 1, 2, 3."

Artemis is amazed, "I do feel better! Thank you, Glory Be!"

Glory Be explains, "Fear can be useful. At times it serves us!

Cars in the street and big animals
should make us nervous."

"Fear and nerves are signals to make us aware.

Those feelings tell us to look out and take extra care!

But worrying *too much* causes discomfort and dread.
No one should live with all that fear in their head!"

"Remember the time you barked at my bear?
But you found out it's stuffed and there's
no need for despair!

Good for you! You overcame that fear!
You're no longer nervous when he is near."

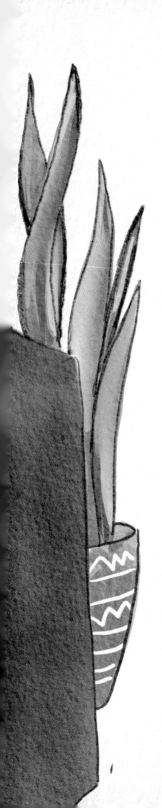

Artemis remembers proudly, "That's right!
Now that old bear never gives me a fright."

Glory Be smiles, "The world is full of mysteries for us to uncover.

We must be safe, but never too scared to go
out and discover!

Come with me, let's be bold and curious!
Soon you'll learn what's harmless and what
should worry us."

Artemis lifts her head, finally calm and understood.
Being accepted and encouraged feels so very good.

Note to Caregivers – Topics to discuss

Fear and anxiety at preschool age is a healthy developmental stage most will go through at different times and to differing degrees.

Sometimes a shy child can become excessively fearful of situations around new people. Turning into a clinging "koala baby", hiding, or refusing to speak to anyone. This behavior can be puzzling and embarrassing if you care what others may think.

It needs to be addressed in a gentle and curious way. Try to allow them to have their feelings, acknowledging the fear and asking, "I see that you are very afraid. What makes this situation scary?" instead of dismissing it and saying, "There's nothing to be scared of."

In this story Glory Be encourages Artemis to talk about her feelings and listens before giving advice. She then reassures her about the partygoers and that she will stay with her and make sure she's not petted if she doesn't want to be. "Not right now" is a good answer for kids to practice.

This is a great time to explain boundaries to kids. They get to choose what's acceptable for them. They can say "No, I don't like that!" and "Please stop!" to anyone and their wishes should be respected. If not, they need to remove themselves from the person or situation.

Kids can be taught how to manage their anxious feelings even if the provoking trigger can't be changed. Much like the sounds of the doorbell and dryer buzzer scaring Artemis. These things will still exist in the house, but Artemis can learn techniques to respond differently.

Did you notice the mom being dismissive and calling Artemis a name?! Even loved ones can be hurtful without meaning to be. Teaching that any feelings are "silly" or unacceptable doesn't help a child learn to deal with them. Accepting and acknowledging feelings teaches children that they are all valid and will pass.

Reminding children about past fears they have conquered validates that they can do it again. Just like Artemis remembered not being afraid of the stuffed bear anymore.

Look for other *Glory Be Stories* coming soon!

Get your **FREE COLORING PAGES** at Geannemeta.com

Go to https://www.geannemeta.com/download-page

to download and print your own Child Safety Plan and Safety Network Pact

This Child Safety Plan helps parents have important conversations with the people who are in their children's lives. It creates a framework for discussing basic safety rules, expectations about supervision, discipline and guarding them against abuse.

About the Author

Geanne Meta

Geanne Meta is a mom to two grownups, and one is a teacher. She enjoys laughing and playing with her granddaughter very much! She also likes to go hiking and camping – preferring a peanut butter cup instead of plain chocolate in her s'mores! Her parenting book, 'Parenting Well After Childhood Abuse: Be a Great Parent Even if Yours Were Crap' has helped many parents with practical advice for raising emotionally healthy kids.

About the Illustrator

Helen Ayle

When I got my first professional watercolor at the age of six, I was so excited, I especially liked the "ultramarine" Cause it sounds so cool, right?! It is a very beautiful color, too. It's like the sky. At some point in my life I thought I needed to choose a "serious" career rather than being an artist, but I'm so glad that I ended up choosing what I love AND making it my job! Besides art I have a whole bunch of things I love doing - like playing piano, watching the sky, hanging out with friends and travelling!

Made in the USA
Coppell, TX
08 December 2022

88123190R10029